"Come and sit on the mat," says Miss Hill.

1

"What did you bring to school, Flick?" says Miss Hill.
Flick has a magnet. "It can pick up pins," she says.

The pins stick to the magnet. The magnet picks up lots of clips too. The children clap.

But Bill is not clapping. He is chatting to Fred.

"Stop chatting to Fred," says
Miss Hill.
"Go and sit next to Jess."

"What did you bring to school, Fred?" says Miss Hill.
Fred has a box of shells.

"I like this smooth pink shell best," he says. The children clap.

But Bill is not clapping. He is chatting to Jess.

"Stop chatting to Jess," says
Miss Hill. "Go and sit next to
the fish tank."

"What did you bring in, Jess?" says Miss Hill.

"This is my pet stick insect," says Jess. "It can lift its left leg."

The stick insect lifts its leg.
The children clap.

But Bill is not clapping. He is chatting to the fish!

"Stop chatting to the fish, Bill," says Miss Hill. "What did you bring in?"

Bill stands up. He has a tooth in his hand.
"Well?" says Miss Hill.
But Bill just stands still.

"Go on," says Miss Hill. "Tell us about the tooth."

"But Miss," says Bill. "You said
I had to stop chatting."